My NEW HOUSE

Franklin Watts

First published in Great Britain in 2018
by The Watts Publishing Group
Copyright © The Watts Publishing Group 2018
All rights reserved

Managing editor: Victoria Brooker
Creative design: Paul Cherrill

ISBN: 978 1 4451 5882 2 (hbk)
ISBN: 978 1 4451 5883 9 (pbk)

Printed in China

Franklin Watts
An imprint of Hachette Children's Group
Part of The Watts Publishing Group
Carmelite House
50 Victoria Embankment
London EC4Y ODZ
An Hachette UK Company

www.hachette.co.uk
www.franklinwatts.co.uk

My NEW HOUSE

Written by
TOM EASTON

Illustrated by
CHARLIE ALDER

FRANKLIN WATTS
LONDON • SYDNEY

Today Mum and Dad gave me some big news.
We're moving to a new house!
"This one is just too small for us now, Rabia," Mum said.
"The new house has a big garden and you won't have
to share a room with Adil anymore."

At first I was very excited. I thought about
having my very own room! I thought about having
a big new garden!

But later I felt sad. I like our house. And what if I wake in the night in the new house and feel lonely because Adil isn't there? And what if there are bears in the garden?

That night I didn't sleep
very well and climbed into
Mum and Dad's bed.

The next morning, Mum noticed I was sad.
"Today I will phone the estate agent,"
she said, "and arrange for us to all go
and see the new house together."

So, after school we did just that, and guess what? The new house is **BRILLIANT**! My room is really big with a window overlooking the garden and Adil is right next door so I can visit him any time I like.

Adil and I checked the garden. "See," he said. "No bears." "That's because they come at night," I said.

We're packing for the move. The house is full of boxes and no-one can find anything. Mum and Dad look a bit tired so Adil and I are keeping out of their hair.

Auntie got us to sort out our old toys and clothes. "It's a good chance to clear out the old things," she said. She told us to make two piles, **THINGS TO KEEP** and **THINGS FOR CHARITY.**

My **KEEP** pile was quite a lot bigger than the **CHARITY** pile.
Mum helped me pack a special bag that has all my most important things
in because it might take a while to unpack in the new house.

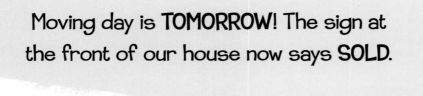

Moving day is **TOMORROW!** The sign at
the front of our house now says **SOLD**.

SOLD

"A new family are
coming to live here,"
Mum said. "They'll look
after it for us."

The rooms look so strange
with no furniture! We had a last
supper in the old house. Auntie went
out and got a takeaway because all
the food was packed!

Moving day was fun but a bit scary.
There were lots of cheery removal men and women
carrying boxes around. They were very
friendly and kept telling jokes.

The new house isn't very far, but we
need a truck to move all the boxes and furniture.
"Is your truck big enough to fit all the boxes in?" I asked one of them.
"I hope so," he said, rubbing his chin.

When I said goodbye to my room, I felt a bit sad again.
Mum gave me a hug. "I'll miss this house, too," she said,
"but the new house will soon feel like home.
Come on, it's time to go now."

I cheered up on the drive to the new house. It felt like we were going on holiday!

When we arrived, I kept getting in the way as the removal team brought boxes into the house.

They all kept saying, "Where do you want this then?"
One of the men brought a box of toys
into my room and I started unpacking it.

It's going to take a long time to unpack all these boxes. Mum said, "Don't worry, Rabia. There's no hurry. We'll be in our new house for a long time."

Mum said I should make myself busy. We found a box of my books and she asked me to put them all on to the book shelf in my room. I have a lot of books!

It took ages to unload the truck and sort out where everything should go. Mum, Dad and Auntie couldn't decide how they wanted the furniture arranged in the sitting room.

Auntie made tea for all the removal people.
They like tea! Adil and I wanted to watch television
but it wasn't plugged in yet. Mum told us to get out of
the way so we went outside to explore the garden.

We searched every inch of the garden, even in the bushes, and finally I was convinced there were NO BEARS.

Finally, all the boxes were in the house
and all the furniture was where it should be.
We waved goodbye to the removal people.

The TV is working but the heating is not. While Mum and Auntie tried to get the heating to work. Adil and I watched a programme.

Dad found the beans and a saucepan and made us all beans on toast!

Mum and Auntie got the heating working eventually!

Then I had my **FIRST** bath in our **NEW** house.
I was a bit sad because we couldn't find the box with the bath toys.

Luckily I had packed
a special bag with all the most
important things in for bed time.

Mum asked me if I wanted a story but I was too excited.

Adil came in and we all talked about the things we will
remember about the old house, and all the exciting
things we are going to do in the new house.

"We can start a veggie patch!" Dad said.

"Once we've found the box with the gardening tools, that is."

I yawned. It had been a big day.
Time for some sleep!
"Good night, Rabia," Mum and Dad
said just before they
turned out the light.

"I'm really going to miss the old house," I said. "But I'm so happy we're all finally here in our **NEW HOUSE!**"

Notes for Parents and Teachers

This book introduces children to the new experience of moving house. This can be a confusing and unsettling experience for the whole family. You may find it useful to take the time to sit and discuss the issues with your child as they come up.

Children may feel anxious before, during and after a move. They may be concerned about losing their possessions, about leaving a comforting and familiar environment for the unknown. The practicalities of the move itself might also be confusing, with children feeling they are unsafe, ignored or in the way.

To prepare your child for the move, visit the new house with him or her. Could you let them choose their own room, or where they'd like their bed in a shared room? Explore the garden together. Walk to the local shops. Practise your route to school to get them used to the new environment and letting them know there will be a new, comfortable routine.

Be honest about the difficulties involved in a move, apologise for not being quite as available as usual, but stress the positives of the move. The new house might have a bigger garden or more bedrooms, or offer new opportunities if moving for work and school. Let your child express his or her concerns and show you are listening and that you understand. If the move is local, perhaps make contact with other children and families near the new house.

Encourage your child to help pack their own possessions so they feel part of the move and in control. Pack a separate 'first night' bag with a favourite teddy, book and night clothes in case you can't find the right box at bedtime.

Your child might like to keep a diary about the moving process, including photos of the old house and the new house. Encourage your child to write down, or talk about, how they feel. What will they miss about the old house, and what are they excited about in the new house? The stories could be added to the diary and taken to school to discuss with the class.

Websites for Parents

www.howstuffworks.com/real-estate/moving-tips/10-tips-for-moving-with-children.htm

www.beafunmum.com/2015/10/tips-for-moving-house-with-children

www.familylives.org.uk/advice/your-family/family-life/how-to-cope-with-moving-house

www.helpiammoving.com/moving_house/moving_with_children.php

www.netdoctor.co.uk/parenting/a9131/moving-house-making-it-less-stressful-for-children

Books To Share

Moving House (Usborne First Experiences)
by Anna Civardi and illustrated by Stephen Cartwright
Usborne Publishing Ltd, 2005

My New Home
by Marta Altés, Macmillan Children's Books, 2015

The Big Day! Moving House
by Nicola Barber, Wayland Books, 2013

Topsy and Tim Move House
by Jean and Gareth Adamson, Ladybird, 2005